Mike Peyton's cartoons are a regular feature in
yachting magazines all over the world.
Throughout the year he runs a 38 foot ketch,
Touchstone, taking out charter parties who
provide him with many of his ideas, and
operating from Maldon, Essex, where he owns
a share of a boatyard. His wife Kathleen, a
best-selling author and erstwhile crew, is now
into horses and riding. Each partner overlaps
on the other's interests sufficiently for them
both to be certain that they have got the best of
the bargain.

They Call It Sailing
Mike Peyton

ISBN 0 333 32215 0

Published in Great Britain 1981 by
NAUTICAL BOOKS
Macmillan London Ltd
4 Little Essex Street
London WC2R 3LF

Associated companies in Auckland, Dallas,
Delhi, Dublin, Hong Kong, Johannesburg,
Lagos, Manzini, Melbourne, Nairobi,
New York, Singapore, Tokyo, Washington
and Zaria

Printed and bound in Great Britain
by Mackays of Chatham Ltd

Contents

Introduction

When the first of these cartoon books was published
– when yachts were gaff rigged and GRP was a
twinkle in a chemist's eye – I seriously believed that it
might make some yachtsman at least realize that he
had made a mistake, and take up some other interest,
something a bit more comfortable such as potholing
or bull-fighting, or less expensive, like polo. However
I now know that this was wishful thinking, and the
unfortunate addict, once hooked on sailing, seldom
kicks the habit.

So I have now resigned myself to trying (as I have
done for years) to avoid the incidents, accidents,
traumas and panics that happen on boats and that
make up the cartoon material, and try instead to
make the best of a bad job by drawing cartoons of the
incidents, accidents, traumas and panics that I
haven't been quick enough to avoid. As the editors
pay me for these cartoons, I can convince myself that
I am providing a service and not sailing solely for my
personal gratification. And I do have some sympathy
with the editors who obviously still think the
cartoons may do some good . . . though personally I
think they haven't a hope in hell.

In the normal course of events

"This is the bit I like, the day before us and not knowing what it is going to offer."

"It was the same last year when they arranged a meet and a dinner dance."

"A stroke of luck, look what I found on the beach."

"A tricolour is it? Usually signifies 'Keep clear of me I am engaged in pair trawling'."

"I've looked it up. Blue and white checks: No!"

"And if you tell me again it's the one sport we can do as a family . . ."

"Hold it steady – it's hot!"

"It's times like this I wish I had spent that tax rebate on a liferaft and not a ghoster."

"Jenks to Enterprise. *Beam me up."*

"It's definitely thickening."

*"I know you say you sail to get away from your wife, but surely
she can't be as bad as this?"*

"Van de Velde, Shipping in a gale off Ostend.*"*

*"I tell you, nothing makes the weather improve quicker than a
bunch of yachtsmen leaving their boats and going back on
the ferry."*

"Did you have to throw him the jib sheet?"

They take it seriously

"Starboard!!!"

"Navigator, would you hand me the race instructions."

"Ready about!!!"

"The results will still be there next weekend, and just as soon."

"That's our gun, Len, but I think they're a bit peeved about waiting for us."

"It might be only a B2 knockdown to you, but it's a bloody capsize to me."

"I said the red one, the RED one . . ."

*"What d'you mean, the wrong mark? Where's that blasted
navigator?!!!"*

"There's times I know I'm a cruising man at heart."

"Tread water, Jim, he was the one we beat in that protest last weekend."

"She's on! Over the side and push her off!! Push, you fool!
Push!!! . . ."
"She's away! Sheet that genny in and let's get this boat
moving . . ."

Ah, les francais!

"Fais attention, Claude!"

"Oui, je vous ai entendu hurler 'Tribord, tribord' . . .
Dommage que vous ne m'ayez pas écouté quand j'ai crié que
j'étais planté . . ."

*"Il a fait deux fois le tour du monde mais il dit que les eaux
françaises sont vraiment trop dangereuses entre le 14 juillet et le
15 août."*

"Ça m'est complètement égal que ce soit exactement comme sur un waterbed . . ."

"C'est quoi être jeune, Henri?"

"T'ai-je jamais dit, Henri, que je ne croyais pas trop en tes dons de navigateur?"

Terra firma

"I tell you, he's from accounts."

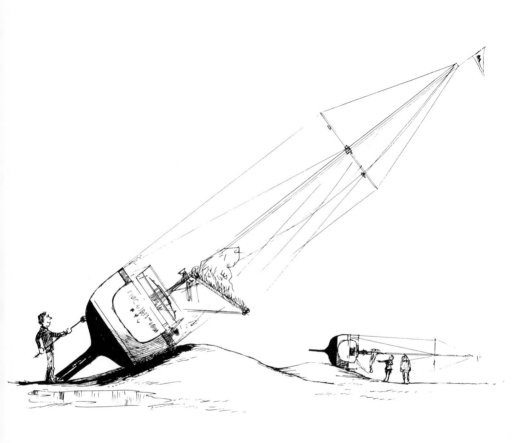

"Well, he's aground and he's not worried."

"And you were worried about using the loo when the tide was out!!!"

"What d'you mean, I can't leave now? Just watch me, mate."

"No mate, there's no law against you lying there, only gravity."

49

"I tell you, if we don't get rid of those leading lights they'll get rid of us."

"I'll sort you out later."

*"I simply told her I wasn't kitted out to make a kitchen shelf and
she went spare."*

Yachtmasters all

"And after you've got the matches, just ask casually what lighthouse it is."

"And stop saying if I was at the navigation class I could ask Mr Hitchins."

"There's the East Knock."

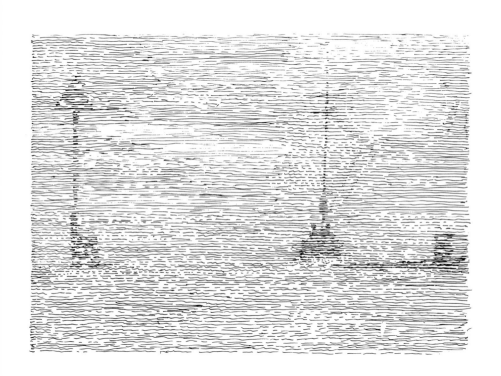

"Relax! Just keep in a fathom and follow the beach around."

"It's a conical, ease your sheets and run off."

"But which one? Alderney, Guernsey, or Jersey?"

"According to my calculations, there's plenty of water."

*"I can do without snide remarks about electrics when I'm doing
the navigation by a buoy flashing one every twenty."*

"Perhaps it shouldn't be the West Crunch according to your calculations, but it is."

"It's okay, we're still in the channel – there's a moored boat
to port."

Meanwhile back at the yard, house, harbour, etc.

*"Unloading? No problem if you use your loaf – slack water, car
at the top of the hard . . ."*

"Look, there's that lovely couple we met in Cherbourg."

"Tide's away, mate."

"There's that stupid ba . . . who rammed us!!!"

"You wouldn't drive forty odd miles in this weather just to pat my bottom."

"It's only temporary. I've been promised a berth next year."

RAMBLING ROSE

"Shut up and let me think."

"Thanks for a super weekend."

"My accountant insisted."

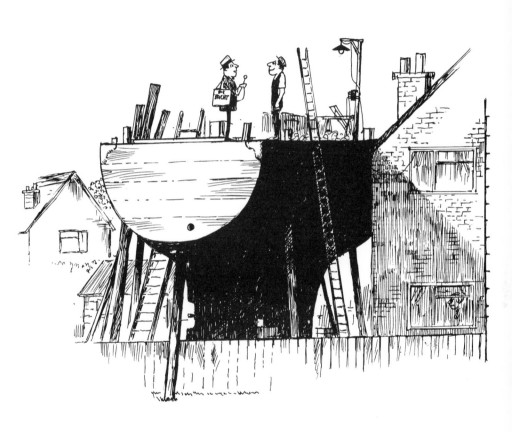

"Have you any other interests?"

"I've fixed it."

"Perhaps it is nicer than doing the ironing, but the ironing will still be there when we get back."

"Okay, take her away."

"Up again, Joe."

"Admitted, there's a few bills outstanding, but it was when he said he didn't trust me that I decided to leave."

These things
do happen

"Pity about the weather, Skip, when we were all geared up to do a good weekend's work."

"It generally starts on the second pull."

"There's a lovely sailing breeze."

*"It's ironic. He always wore a size too large so that he could
kick them off."*

"I've told you before not to hitch it to the backstay."

"That bar isn't as bad as the pilot makes out."

"What's the hold up?!!"

"Ready about, lee ho!"

"Keep her on this tack, Peter, until I serve the soup."

"They do it often, but I can never understand why."

"My vessel is healthy, my foot."

"Robert, old boy! What a pleasant surprise!"

*"The coastguard says the front one has the narrow end at
the top."*

"Relax! No other fools will be sailing in this fog . . ."